S0-BCW-344

HUMOR: ANATOMY OF THE FUNNY BONE

Written By
Bud Nelson

Illustrated By
Stanley Tang

Contributing Illustrator
Linda Negley

Kathy Kolbe Concept, Inc.
Phoenix, Arizona

TEACHING GUIDE

The humorous slant and open-ended activities of this Think-ercise® combine in a highly motivating approach that involves students in writing, researching, designing and drawing. Encouraging investigation into various forms of humor, the book lends itself to discussion and debate of language, ideas and issues.

Multi-level in difficulty, HUMOR is designed to accommodate a broad range of interests, ages and abilities. Activities need not be done sequentially. Instead, self-selection from the options is encouraged as such decision making is an important part of internalizing the lessons.

Sure to spark discussion as well as laughter, HUMOR can be easily adapted to meet individual or group needs. It can be introduced as the basis for long-term assignments and independent projects or for mental warm-ups and extension activities. It offers participatory reading which involves readers in analyzing and evaluating others' humor. Students use creative thinking skills to concoct jokes, puns and stories in oral, written and non-verbal modes of communication.

Activities in HUMOR provide a variety of experiences addressing the different propensities and needs of the conations identified by the Intellectual Fitness (IF) Profile™ of Wonderlic-Kolbe Conations. Conations are thinking styles or mental tendencies manifested in problem-solving situations.

Opening up broad possibilities for examining the topic of humor, the book has numerous applications in all content areas: language arts, social studies, science or math. In any classroom, HUMOR can become the catalyst for unifying group effort, fostering socialization and initiating team interaction.

INVENTORY OF EXCELLENCE™

Kathy Kolbe Concept Think-ercises contain results-oriented techniques to develop critical and creative thinking, communication skills and foster growth in self-esteem. In the Kathy Kolbe Concept, excellence takes on substance, becomes observable and can be taught. The Think-ercise HUMOR was designed to include all the areas in the Kathy Kolbe Concept Inventory of Excellence, as shown on the following page. Listed in detail are all the critical and creative thinking skills. The Inventory of Excellence also encompasses all the affective behaviors as well as verbal, visual and other sensory communication skills.

1984 Edition
® MCMLXXXII Kathy Kolbe
All rights reserved
ISBN 0-86680-050-6

Published by Kathy Kolbe Concept, Inc.
P.O. Box 15050
Phoenix, Arizona 85060

for the book "HUMOR: ANATOMY OF THE FUNNY BONE"

INVENTORY OF EXCELLENCE™
Thinking Strengths

CRITICAL (convergent/logical)

Knowledge/Comprehension
math
Graphing, estimation, deductive reasoning, making inferences

science
Observation of characteristics, classifying, predicting developments, hypothesizing

social studies
Group cooperation in making up jokes and stories, socialization, team interaction, researching origins of jokes, analyzing cultural humor, information gathering

language arts
Writing and telling jokes, riddles, puns, limericks, fables, phonetic stories; listening skills, descriptive writing, titling, verbalization of ideas, vocabulary in context, analogies and similes, research techniques

Application—use information
Reinterpreting knowledge in humorous fashion; applying information to complete tasks

Analysis—take apart
Taking apart elements of humor, analyzing what makes something funny, decoding data to use in making jokes, classifying characteristics for caricatures, comparing possible outcomes, deciding on approaches, observing similarities and differences, ordering events

Synthesis—put together in a new way
Reconstructing jokes with variations, altering a "straight" story to make it humorous, composing scenarios with certain components, designing cartoons, putting together different elements to make a joke or story

Evaluation—assess
Critiquing others' humor, evaluating own efforts at humor, setting up criteria for humor "in good taste," deciding on appropriateness, judging how well ideas work, weighing alternatives

CREATIVE (divergent/intuitive)

Fluency—many
Thinking of many humorous responses; having lots of ideas for funny jokes, puns, stories; seeing a variety of ways to make something funny, creating many humorous characters

Flexibility—adapt
Looking at things in a different way to find humor, adapting stories to humorous approach, finding a variety of ways to be funny, redirecting efforts, using different approaches

Originality—unique
Coming up with unusual jokes or puns, thinking of clever ways to be funny, finding humor in unobvious places, completing tasks with unique methods, offering novel variations on projects

Elaboration—add to
Embellishing on jokes and humorous stories, adding detail to make something funnier, expanding on a humorous idea, building in personal ideas, embroidering a small incident into a funny tale

Risk Taking—guess
Daring to try a difficult form of humor, risking that no one will laugh, experimenting with different kinds of humor, predicting people's reactions, exploring possibilities, trying new approaches when the outcome is unclear

Complexity—capsulize
Structuring material into humorous forms, capsulizing information in verbal and visual presentations, dealing with a number of alternatives, finding order in unrelated data

Curiosity—wonder
Wondering what makes something funny, following a hunch, pondering impacts, pursuing an inquiry approach, questioning information, puzzling about people's reactions to jokes

Imagination—visualize
Fantasizing movie and TV show scenarios, dreaming up humorous characters and story lines, visualizing results if certain factors are changed, conjuring mental images of events

Affective Behaviors: *Humor* builds self-esteem as the result of creative efforts others can see, hear and appreciate. It requires cooperation, elicits responsiveness, initiates responsible approaches, leads to ethical analysis, fosters independence and enhances empathy.

TABLE OF CONTENTS

Foreword v
In Defense of the Funny Bone 1
History of Humor 5
Let's Get Scientific 17
Funny Characters 25
Build Your Own Crazy Jokes 43
Humor In Poetry — Poetry In Humor 49
Puns 55
Knock-Knocks
The Puns' Country Cousins 61
Whimsy 69
Caricatures & Cartoons 77
Embellishments In Humor 85
Don't Like The Movies? Write Your Own! . . 89
Picturesque Speech — Similes 99
Stereotypes In Humor 103
Slapstick Humor
And Other Forms of Violence 111
The Ultimate Craziness
Or The Phonetic Story 114
Anudder Joke 118

About the Author . . .

Bud Nelson explains his omnivorous interests by saying, "Inside this old hulk is a young boy, still eager to learn about the world and how it works."

The young boy is most apparent, perhaps, when Bud is hand-casting and painting lead soldiers. The pride and joy of this history buff is his colorful array of knights, numbering over 1,300.

"You wake up at night and hear the footsteps of 2,600 little feet; it's scary," he claims. An infantry combat veteran, this ex-paratrooper picked up a Bachelor's degree in Economics, a Master's in Business Administration, a football letter, a dramatics award, and a Phi Beta Kappa Key.

After some years in the business world, he served over ten years in state government before returning to the private sector.

His hobbies include donating blood, writing poetry, collecting all sorts of things, and helping old ladies across the street, whether they wish to go or not.

Known across the country as a raconteur, Bud is much in demand as a Master of Ceremonies and banquet speaker.

In Defense of the Funny Bone

"The existence of a funny bone in Homo Sapiens is proof that man descended not from the ape, but from the hyena."
Dr. Katerina Wunderlich,
Berlin Institute of Psychiatric Anomalies

"The fact that the funny bone exists only while a person is alive is a well-known fact. No autopsy has turned one up. Rather than challenging its existence, the researchers could better spend their time figuring out how the funny bone leaves the body upon the demise of its host."
Professor Hiram Blotnik,
University of Montenegro School of Medicine

*"The funny bone is **not** the skull. The skull is the source, not of funnyness, but of silliness."*
Dr. Alois Schickelgruber,
Vienna College of Brain Surgery
and Sausage Making

1

"One of the saddest birth defects is to be born without a funny bone. Career paths are very limited for such poor souls. They will probably grow up to be parents."
Jane Fonder,
Southern California College
of Where It's At

I'm sorry to say, your son – was born without a funnybone

"The Greeks had a word for it, but it escapes me for the moment." — Daniel Webster, Author

"The funny bone is connected through the nervous system to the ear, the eye, the facial muscles, and the belly. And, occasionally to the brain."
Dr. Lucky Luciano,
College of Hard Knox

2

"History has shown that no one with a funny bone ever went hungry. Starved to death, sure, but never went hungry!" — Friar Tuck
Colonel Sanders School
of Gastronomy

LARGEST AWARD EVER
IN PERSONAL INJURY CASE

Axgrinder, Utah, Sept. 26(API). A circuit judge today handed down the largest award ever granted in a personal injury case in the U.S. Homer V. Smedberry convinced the judge that his funny bone had been destroyed in a January 4th auto accident. The driver of the other car, Luke Henhus, has been ordered to pay Smedberry $27,000,000 in cash, plus twelve lords a-leaping, eleven ladies dancing, ten pipers piping, nine drummers drumming, eight maids a-milking, seven swans a-swimming, six geese a-laying, five golden rings, four calling birds, three French hens, two turtle doves and a partridge in a pear tree. Asked what had influenced his decision in his landmark case, Judge Renfro Bilgeswisher said, "Gee, I dunno."

3

The expurgated, original words to the song, "Dry Bones":

"Oh, the foot bone connected to the leg bone; the leg bone connected to the neck bone; the neck bone connected to the ear bone; the ear bone connected to the funny bone."

I liked it better that way.

HISTORY OF HUMOR

"ABANDON ALL SERIOUSNESS, YE WHO ENTER HERE" — Buddius Burtonus, 200 B.C.(?)

Humor has probably been around about as long as there have been people on this Earth. The fact that we don't have well-documented examples of humor from 12,000 years ago or more could be a matter of our lack of perception of the clues before us, rather than their non-existence.

We could have a lot of examples of early humor lying around without recognizing them as such. You've probably seen pictures of those stone and pottery figures of fat women found in caves and ancient settlement diggings. Anthropologists and archaeologists have strongly suggested that they are symbols of fertility, offerings to the Goddess of Fertility, or representations of the Goddess of Fertility herself. But, what if they're wrong? Perhaps

5

they are only sculptors' renditions of ancient man's recurrent one-liner, "My mother-in-law is *so* fat that . . . !" Isn't it just possible that virtually every community had an overweight woman that someone was poking fun at?

MONSTER-IN-LAW

And, think about the ancient grotesque carvings that are supposedly representative of this god or that spirit. Isn't it just possible the high priest or chief or mayor or landlord had a big nose or bulging eyes or floppy ears or long tongue (or any combination thereof) and was immortalized in a sculptor's caricature?

Some of the funny-looking animals and people drawn on cave walls may have been *meant* to look funny, so other cave dwellers would look at them, shake their heads, grin, and say to themselves, "Look at that goofy looking Mastodon! Oog is sure a crazy artist!"

We shouldn't be surprised if the earliest example of writing on the wall of some as-yet-undiscovered cave is translated to read:

First Caveman: Why did the Tyrannosaurus Rex swim across the river?

Second Caveman: To get to the other side.

Since the human brain has been at or about its present size for many centuries, it is safe to assume that our ancient forebears used a part of their brain for poking fun at themselves, each other, and the world around them. Incongruity has always accompanied the human condition. There have always been people who are taller ("How's the weather up there?"), shorter ("Excuse me, are you standing in a hole?"), thinner ("You wouldn't see him at all if he stood sidewise."), fatter ("Have you ever considered renting yourself out as a mountain?"), prettier ("I love my wife, but oh, you kid!"), and uglier ("That face would stop a sun dial!").

Aesop used humor to get his points of morality across. Humor was his way of seizing and holding the listeners' attention. He often resorted to talking animals. (In his time they spoke Ancient Greek; in my experience, they all speak English.) People remembered his humorous fables, and that helped remind them of the "moral of the story" which he tacked to the end of each fable.

Great men have enjoyed humor and depended upon humor to relieve the tensions of their burden of responsibilities. Abraham Lincoln resorted to humor to overcome hostility; to win the attention of audiences and juries; and to give convincing examples to support arguments which he made in courtrooms and political debates. Perhaps his passion for humorous writings and anecdotes helped

9

him lead his country through its darkest years. His habit of poking fun at himself, his back-country roots and homely appearance stood him in good stead when, as President, he was caricatured cruelly by the press. After all, they were only doing to him what he had been doing to himself for years.

There are many pictures of President Franklin Roosevelt taken during the dreary years of the Great Depression and the perilous years of World War II, showing him, head thrown back, teeth flashing, as he roared with laughter at some joke. His favorite reaction to a joke was the cry, "Don't you just love it? Don't you just love it?"

People have lavished love and favor on comedy and comedians since early times. Perhaps no symbol of this favor stands out in history more clearly than the court jester, the "fool," or the "Merry Andrew." This historic companion of the ruler might have been a dwarf, a midget, or a misshapen person; but more often than not, he (there is no tradition of female jesters) was a normal-looking person with a gift of wit, music, agility, and *perception.* Woe to the entertainer who failed to entertain! And perceiving what amused or pleased the master was the first and main order of business. This worthy individual became a member of the court, ate well, slept warm, and was relieved of the drudgery which was the lot of all except the nobility. Comedy was a popular part of the theater down through the years, and successful comedians reaped the fruits of public favor. Today, we reward our comedians (and, finally, our comediennes) of stage, screen, radio, and television with huge salaries and public

adulation. They have largely supplanted the humorous books and magazines of the past. Writers of humorous materials now aspire to have their words uttered by leading comedians and comediennes rather than have them appear in print.

To exercise *your* sense of humor, try to make up a joke about life in the time of the Neanderthals. Remember, there are very few artifacts beyond spears, clubs, and stones. No roads for chickens to cross, no pants for suspenders to hold up, no president to poke fun at.

For Instance:

First Neanderthal Man: I went out and clubbed a wife last night, but now I'm not so sure I want to keep her.

Second Neanderthal Man: Which club did you use?

First Neanderthal Man: My Number One club.

Second Neanderthal Man: That's probably your trouble. You should have used your putter.

Now, your turn:

_____

_____

_____

_____

_____

_____

_____

_____

_____

_____

_____

_____

_____

Next, assuming that either gender could be a court jester, cast yourself in that role. What kind of jester would you be? What role would you assume if your life (or your livelihood) depended on it?

I'm just a wild and crazy guy!

Would you dance, sing, tell jokes? Would you be silly, or would you resort to satire, perhaps, in an attempt to influence the ruler's policies? Try it out on a friend or parent.

_____

_____

_____

_____

_____

_____

_____

_____

_____

_____

Finally, become a latter-day Aesop and write a moral fable. It can be no more serious than being on time for class or picking up your room, but use appropriate animals in your fable. (Have them speak English.)

_____

_____

_____

_____

_____

_____

_____

_____

_____

LET'S GET SCIENTIFIC

"FOR IN ALL SCIENCE THERE IS HUMOR, AND IN ALL HUMOR THERE IS SCIENCE. OR IS IT THE OTHER WAY AROUND?" — L. Bert Eisenstein

Everyone has a sense of humor. That's one way of saying that every normal person appreciates what humor is, or can detect humor in a given situation, condition, or statement. Not everyone has this sense to the same degree. Some seem to fail to see the humor in anything, while at the other extreme, there are people who see humor in *everything*. We are most at ease with people who are at neither end of the scale, but who are somewhere in the middle of the population. Figure 1 is a statistical curve representative of the population's (any sizeable population's) sense of humor:

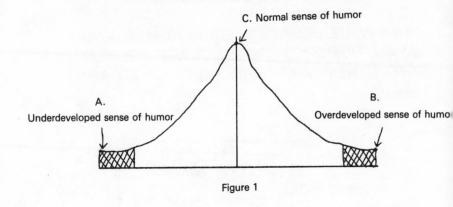

C. Normal sense of humor

A.
Underdeveloped sense of humor

B.
Overdeveloped sense of humor

Figure 1

The segments of the curve in Figure 1 can best be characterized as:

A. Those who feel that the world is a grim place, and there is virtually nothing funny about any part of it. These people are characterized by pale skin, hollow (often piercing) eyes, frowns, hollow laughter, thin bodies, and ulcers.

B. Those who think everything is an absolute scream. For instance, if someone says "Good morning" to them they dissolve into a gelatinous blob, and cry "Did you hear that? She said 'Good morning'! Hah, hah, hah! 'Good morning'! For crying out loud! That's a great one! Hah, hah, hah! 'Good morning'! Where does she get her material? Hah, hah, hah!" These people are characterized by ruddy skin, bulging (often glassy) eyes, big grins, high-

18

pitched laughter, chunky bodies, and thin friends with ulcers.

C. US

Try writing dialog for a scene involving an A, B and C.

_____

_____

_____

_____

_____

_____

_____

_____

_____

_____

_____

_____

_____

_____

Let us now pursue some of the theories of Dr. L. Bert Eisenstein. He maintained that you could chart reaction curves to certain types of humor. His first example was the "Neutral Reaction Curve". Here, you tell a joke, and you get a neutral reaction, as in Figure 2.

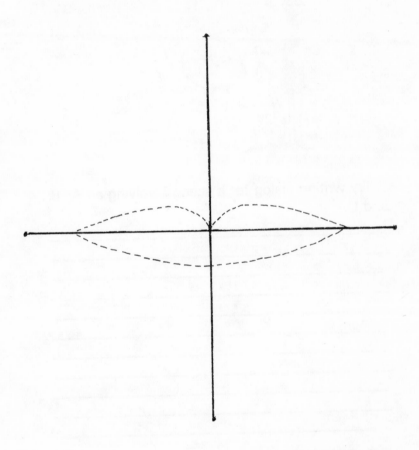

The best example of a neutral reaction would be telling a joke in English to a group of Mongolian Yurt salesmen.

The next Eisenstein example is the "Negative Reaction Curve". Here the bulk of the population sees the humor in your joke, but your delivery leaves something to be desired, and you've lost the audience at both ends of the statistical curve, as in Figure 3.

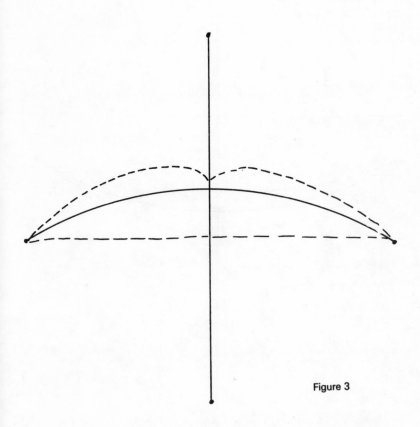

Figure 3

Figure 4 is an illustration of Dr. Eisenstein's "Positive Reaction Curve", the aim of all humorists. In this example, your humor might be lost on some of the population in the middle, but you've picked up a more positive reaction at both ends of the population curve, and you get the following result:

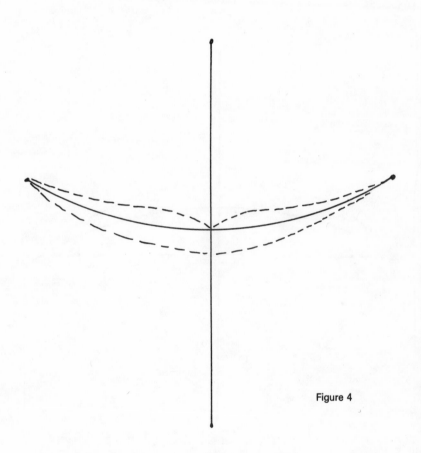

Figure 4

22

May all your attempts at humor be rewarded with POSITIVE REACTION CURVES!

Now it's your turn. Show and explain a Delayed Reaction Curve. Any other reaction curves you'd care to add?

FUNNY CHARACTERS

For some reason, it seems that certain names or places are funnier than others. They sound funny by themselves, or they conjure up a humorous connotation. Names that mean substantially the same thing don't always have the same effect on our funny bones. For instance, "gorge" is not funny, nor is "ravine", but "gulch" is. If you want a funny locale for a story, set it in a town with "gulch" in its name. "Drover's Gulch", for example.

"Prairie" is not funny, nor is "plains"; but "flats" is. I wonder why? "Crossing" is not particularly amusing, but "corners" conjures up a kind of funny backwoodsiness.

Mixing nationalities can reveal names that are funny to one nationality or culture, and yet not at all funny to another! I went to school with kids named Swick and Stank, both perfectly legitimate names. But a lot of people thought them funny. How about Suchanek? I worked with him. He thought Mishmash was a funny name. I told him that someone looking through the phone book and coming across his name would exclaim, "Such a neck!". He didn't think that was funny. He pronounced his name "Soo-chan'-eck."' The Mangiaracina family ran a grocery store in my home town. What's funny about "Mangiaracina"? It means "eat grapes".

Peoples' names are the same. Some names just sound sort of funny on their own. In my old home town's telephone directory, I found two families named Mishmash. I never met a Mishmash, but I always thought the name was funny. They probably didn't.

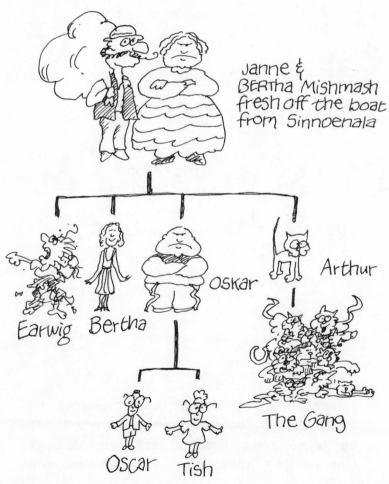

Janne & BERTha Mishmash fresh off the boat from Sinnoenala

Earwig   Bertha   Oskar   Arthur

Oscar   Tish   The Gang

In my current phone book, I've found "Ding", "Dong", and "Bell". Wouldn't that be a great name for a doorbell company or something? And I found "Lie", "Gip", and "Steele". Sounds like a law firm in a Marx Brothers comedy, doesn't it? "Fish", "Fowle", and "Katz" might consider going into the pet shop business. Your own telephone book doubtless contains a gold mine of names for you to combine in all manner of ways.

Generalizations are dangerous to make, but I had always thought that names beginning with the letter "Q" were considered funnier than names beginning with any other letter. Don't ask me why.

Perhaps they are just relatively rare. But, I'm hard pressed to come up with examples. My phone book yields "Quackenbush" (Who can forget Groucho Marx as Dr. Quackenbush?), and "Quigley" (Don Adams used that name in his material). Aside from them, I can only come up with "Quackenberry" (obviously, the product of a Quackenbush.) "Quimby" is not too unfunny, I guess. "Quist" might be funny to you, but it's a very common name in my Swedish background.

If you wanted to make up a funny character, you probably wouldn't want to use a name like John Brown from Waltham, Massachusetts. You'd be better off going with Homer Quackenberry from Mishmash Corners, Iowa. (Iowa is funny, Massachusetts is not.)

29

You can create your own funny characters from the lists below. Take one from each column at random.

A	B	C	D
FIRST NAME	LAST NAME	CITY	STATE
Abner	Clawhammer	Bull's Mill	Arkansas
Esmeralda	Crabapple	Cripple Creek	Idaho
Hector	Frampton	Farmer's Flats	Iowa
Hooter	Goober	Garley's Gulch	Kansas
Jethro	Hornblower	Hayfork	Kentucky
Maizie	Klotz	Horseburg	Mississippi
Minnie	Quagmire	Sorghum	Missouri
Myrtle	Quigley	Swinetown	Nebraska
Pearly Sue	Quirk	Wart Hollow	Oklahoma
Phinneas	Strump	Water Hole	South Dakota
Zebulon	Windflower	Yukey's Corners	Tennessee

After you've run through the many combinations available in the example above, start your own "Build-A-Funny-Character" game by coming up with lists of funny first names, last names, cities and states. It'll be more fun if you do it list by list, rather than character by character, because you will find the random combinations funnier than your deliberate choices.

30

You can involve others in this game by having each make out one of the lists, and reading them off in rotation sequence for some hilarious combinations.

A FIRST NAME	B LAST NAME
_____	_____
_____	_____
_____	_____
_____	_____
_____	_____
_____	_____
_____	_____
_____	_____
_____	_____
_____	_____
_____	_____
_____	_____

C CITY	D STATE
_____	_____
_____	_____
_____	_____
_____	_____
_____	_____
_____	_____
_____	_____
_____	_____
_____	_____
_____	_____
_____	_____
_____	_____

31

Enlist your family or friends in a search through the telephone book for names you consider humorous. Depending on your culture, you will find humor where others would not. If your group could include people from all corners of the world, you would be hard pressed to get a consensus on whether or not a chosen name is humorous or not.

Names that may not be humorous by themselves can become knee slappers in a different context.

What's in a name? Well, looking in the newspaper for name coincidences can turn up some funny situations. *J. Michael Love,* chairman of the New Hampshire Public Utilities Commission, was appointed to his post on Valentine's Day. I just read that *Dr. Neil Gesundheit* is chief medical resident in a California hospital. Do you suppose he specializes in respiratory diseases or allergies?

In my home town, we had a used car lot run by the *Crooks* brothers. Their motto was, "Buy Your Car From Crooks". No comment. For awhile, *Dr. Skaar* was our family physician. We also knew a dentist named *Dr. Pang.* Their choice of profession was dictated at birth, I guess.

I've also heard of dentists named *Paine, Toothacher, Yankum and Gumm*, but I can't swear to their authenticity. The yellow pages of the phone book, however, yielded the names of *Bicandi* (it'll help his business) and *Chu* (he'll help you) under "Dentists". I was so intrigued by my discovery, I cruised through the "Attorneys" and "Physicians" listings, too.

I ran across some interesting names. Under "Physicians" I found:

Dr. Avakoff	— Obviously a cold specialist?
Dr. Comfort	— Great bedside manner?
Dr. Fee	— First things first?
Dr. Gabby	— Puts you at your ease?
Dr. Goodfriend	— What more can we say?
Dr. Grieff	— A lot of that going around?
Dr. Oral	— As in Dr. Oral, Surgeon? or?
Dr. Orcutt	— Is that a good alternative?
Dr. Payne	— Should he go in business with Dr. Grieff or Dr. Comfort? Payne & Grieff or Paine & Comfort?
Dr. Posthumus	— A forensic pathologist?
Dr. Sawn	— Should he go in business with Dr. Orcutt?
Dr. Stich	— Need we say more?
Dr. Tong	— Dare we ask?
Dr. Trueblood	— A serologist?
Dr. Zitman	— Specializing in adolescents' complexions?

All of the above are genuine names, taken from the yellow pages of my local phone books. I mean no disrespect to the persons involved, but their names, coupled with their professions, do conjure up some pictures in our minds. I must say their names yielded a more fruitful source than did the "Dentists" lists.

My appetite whetted, I turned to the listings of "attorneys". There I found:

Mr. Chase — No ambulances, we hope.

Mr. Daschbach — More about him below.

Mr. Eagle — Would you call him a legal-eagle?

Mr. Eshoo — I think he picked the wrong profession. He should have been a doctor, teamed up with Dr. Gesundheit (above) and founded the Eshoo-Gesundheit Respiratory Diseases Clinic.

Mr. Justman — A clear-cut favorite to rise to the top of his profession, the U.S. Supreme Court!

Mr. Ketchum — Should form a law firm with two attorneys listed above. The firm would be known as Chase, Ketchum and Daschbach!

Mr. Law — This man's name was Benjamin, but I just remembered I knew a lawyer in Illinois named Robert Law. Their choice of profession could well have been dictated by their last name, but I never met a doctor named Medicine.

Mr. Lynch — We hope he puts a stop to it!

Mr. Toothman — No comment. I only wish I'd found him on the lists of dentists.

Mr. Trusty — I'd hire him, wouldn't you?

Mr. Wiseman — Obviously, Mr. Justman's rival for that Supreme Court job.

JOHN JUSTMAN
ATTORNEY
AT
LAST!

So, there you are: the results of not-so-extensive research. You can do it, too. Every town has yellow pages, and you can search out names that either fit the profession in some way, or put a person in the wrong profession (Messrs. Eshoo and Toothman, for example). You can also do it with others. If everyone in a group has the same telephone directory, go through them together, and see who can spot the related or unrelated names. Some of you are going to have a surprise. It will become obvious to you that we are neighbors, because you are going to find all the names listed above in *your* telephone books!

Of course, you can dispense with the yellow pages altogether, and create characters around names chosen from the white pages.

Mr. Bright	His mother called him Sonny. (Sunny)
Mr. Cannon	He's a big gun at the office.
Mr. Bishop	He's holier than thou.
Mr. Hewitt	Probably started out as a lumberjack.

PLEASE MR. BRIGHT, TURN OFF YOUR Teeth!

You fill in a description for the following:

Miss Kluck	_____
Ms. Piz	_____
Mr. DeLong	_____
Miss Quepon	_____
Mr. Breedlove	_____
Mr. Rusher	_____
Miss Showers	_____
Ms. Backus	_____
Mrs. Bacon	_____
Mr. Buttermore	_____
Ms. Greathouse	_____
Dr. Best	_____
Dr. Goodman	_____
Mrs. Specks	_____
Mr. Cox	_____

Mr. Tinker _____

Miss Peacock _____

Dr. Katz _____

Ms. Bratt _____

Mr. Eek _____

Mr. Backoff _____

Miss Cryer _____

Dr. Carver _____

Mr. Fixman _____

Ms. Handlong _____

Mr. Heid _____

Ms. Heguy _____

Mr. Lyman _____

Mr. Byers _____

Mr. Klimback _____

Mr. Bahlman _____

Mr. Solvit _____

Miss Shortsleeves _____

There's no limit to the things you can do with names. Another activity is to fit book titles with humorous names for authors. A real example is a book named *How Does Your Garden Grow,* by *D. Weed.* Make up a title that will fit a celebrity author, or make up an author who will fit a title. For instance:

Back to the Soil	*Sam Spade*
The Split Seam	*Brooke Shields*
One Man for Life	*Liz Taylor*
Play for Fun	*Magic Johnson*
Early to Bed	*Johnny Carson*

Or, turn it around the other way and make up fictional authors for book titles:

Invest for Tomorrow   *Lotta Kasch*

38

Eat and Lose Weight	*Ima Hogg*
Get Smart, Get Rich	*I. Reed Daley*
American Getaway	*Ron Luce*
You Can Do It If You Try	*Will Power*

Finally, a few words about name perceptions and the use of names in writing. Authors over the years have used name choice to convey instant impressions. The examples are endless, but my favorite is perhaps the unfortunate Mr. Ichabod Crane in *The Legend of Sleepy Hollow*. The name alone conjures up a picture of a rather timorous, frail soul, doesn't it? Voltaire's *Candide* presents us with Doctor Pangloss who did just that, glossed over every evil he encountered. As you read, notice the names of the characters, and see if the authors didn't choose names that reflected the attributes of the various characters. Look out for the few, however, who used "reverse English" and gave their villains virtuous-sounding names.

39

You don't have to rely on reading to do this analysis, however. The movies and television will do it for you on two levels. First, the characters in the shows tend to have names that "fit" the characters. Would Archie Bunker be the same if his name were Percy Sweetwater? Would *Hart to Hart* be written about a married couple named Schwarzenegger? No offense, Arnold!

On the second level, we have the names of the actors themselves. They used to say they changed their names to fit onto the marquees, although Freddie Bartholomew never did. (Of course, his star set early, didn't it?) But most of our heroes and heroines of stage, screen and television bobbed their names to fit our pre-conceptions of what a star's name *ought* to be, and you know what the result has been. Would Bò Derek have starred in *"10"* if her name had been Coramae Derrick? Or Bertha Derekstrom? The next time you see the cast of characters of a film or play, look for the drumbeat names. They go *Boom Boom, Boom Boom-Boom, BoomBoom Boom, or BoomBoom Boom-Boom,* but very, *very* seldom more drumbeats than that.

BUILD YOUR OWN CRAZY JOKES

Jokes are really only short stories with a humorous twist to them. They contain one or more characters, a situation, and an outcome. Generally, the joke is structured with a cast of characters which fits the situation, and an outcome which, though often unexpected, fits the character(s) and the situation. For example:

A young man came to work every day with a carrot behind his ear. His co-workers withheld comment for several weeks, but one day he showed up with a wiener behind his ear. Unable to contain herself any longer, a young stenographer demanded, "What's going on? For weeks you've been coming to work every day with a carrot behind your ear, and today you've got a wiener behind your ear! Why?" "Simple," the young man replied, "When I looked in the refrigerator this morning, I found I was all out of carrots."

That joke, as outrageous as it may be, is acceptable because the parts fit: the characters, the situation, and the outcome. But what if his answer had been, "That was no lady, that was my wife"? It would have defied the normal formula, but it could be funny for that very reason. So what could happen if you took normal characters, situations and outcomes, and mixed them in a random madness? You'd get crazy jokes, that's what.

Below, and on the next page, are the ingredients for a build-your-own crazy joke project. As in the crazy character game, selecting from each column at random can result in some far-out humor. Fill in the blanks of the following joke with selections from the columns below it. With fourteen to choose from in each column, the combinations are seemingly endless:

One day, a _____ showed up for _____ wearing _____. When the _____ objected, _____ jumped up and said, "_____ _____."

COLUMN A	COLUMN B	COLUMN C
ballerina	a physical	a frown
bulb snatcher	bowling	a grin
bus driver	church	a lavalier
clown	final exams	a mini-skirt
doctor	jury duty	a mink coat
librarian	lunch	a parachute
lion tamer	school	a saddle
midget	study hall	a spiked helmet
minister	swimming class	cowboy boots
nurse	target practice	earmuffs
Scotchman	the big game	long, green hair
secretary	the matinee	one red sock,
sophomore	the take-off	one blue sock
toad	work	overalls
		a top hat and tails

COLUMN D	COLUMN E
chimney sweep	a bystander
conductor	a clam digger
diamond cutter	a hippopotamus
district attorney	a meter reader
hall monitor	a pastry cook
hangman	a pole vaulter
head waiter	a portrait artist
horse trainer	a traffic cop
jockey	a waitress
plumber	the bishop
sign painter	the hostess
snake charmer	the Prince of Wales
trapeze artist	the principal
well digger	the undertaker

COLUMN F

A fool and his money are soon parted.

Close the cover before striking.

He's a typical gnu, and a tiler, too.

If it doesn't work, we'll give you your money back.

It's to hold his pants up.

Loose lips sink ships.

Oh, he's not so shaggy.

On the whole, I'd rather be in Philadelphia.

Remember the Alamo!

She wanted to get to the other side.

That was no lady, that was my wife.

There's no accounting for taste.

There's probably another pair at home just like it.

What's a nice girl like you doing in a place like this?

After you've had some solitary fun with this, enlist your family or friends in the game. From two to six can play. A moderator should read the joke out loud, with the other players filling in the blanks in turn. This can be done by reading an assigned number down from the top or up from the bottom, completely at random, or written on slips of paper. In any event, the results can be hilarious.

One day, a _____ showed up for_____ wearing _____. When the _____ objected, _____ jumped up and said, "_____ _____."

One day, a _____ showed up for_____ wearing _____. When the _____ objected, _____ jumped up and said, "_____ _____."

One day, a _____ showed up for_____ wearing _____. When the _____ objected, _____ jumped up and said, "_____ _____."

Once you've got the idea, you or your group can make out your own lists of people, events, things, and sayings, and expand the number of combinations still further. Types of characters or particular persons can be included to bring the humor closer to your experience.

WHO   WHAT   WHEN   WHERE   WHY   HOW

_____

_____

_____

_____

_____

_____

_____

_____

_____

_____

After you've used the joke format above with your own sets of columns, branch out further by composing your own skeleton format. You can even use nursery rhymes with hilarious results after you've exhausted your old jokes inventory.

_____

_____

_____

_____

_____

_____

HUMOR IN POETRY
POETRY IN HUMOR

Humorists have used poetry, and poets have used humor, since the birth of the two art forms many centuries ago. Poets can't be bemoaning their lost loves forever, and humorists can't forever resist the humorous rhyme, so the marriage was inevitable.

Here's one:

I'm tired of my centipede named Toulouse;
As a pet, he should be replaced.
It's not just the money I spend for his shoes;
It's the time I spend keeping them laced.

Tie your
Shoelaces!

Crazy? Of course. But, if I don't buy him shoes,
he refuses to go to dancing class.

You've got a pet, real or fancied, that you can write a short poem about, haven't you? How about:

I had a little puppy,
I taught him how to play.
Now he's grown up and wears a leash
And drags me every day.

Ogden Nash was a successful humorist-poet. He was an oddity, because he was successful in a medium when very few poets could scratch out a living at their craft. I can still remember the delight I had when I read his humorous poetry. I would suggest you give him a try. He wrote some serious poetry, too, but he'll always be remembered for making people laugh. He became such a celebrity, in fact, that he made radio and television appearances. Well, for every Ogden Nash, I guess there are about 50 million of us that write a few lines of funny doggerel once in a while. Such as:

Hannah the Hippo bemoans her loss;
She loved a giraffe so high.
He finally gave her the gate because
They couldn't see eye to eye.

50

Of course, limericks are always humorous. I can't recall even one, offhand, that wasn't at least *meant* to be funny. Limericks have changed over the years. In times gone by, the first line was repeated as the last line. I consider this a cop-out, because there was one less rhyme to come up with. For instance, I'll show you a limerick in the old style, and then try to come up with the different last line, which is common today.

Okay, old style:

There once was a lawyer named Wise
Who was cursed with two badly-crossed eyes.
He poured most of his grog
On the floor for the dog
This unfortunate lawyer named Wise.

Now, new style, more difficult:

There once was a lawyer named Wise
Who was cursed with two badly-crossed eyes.

He poured most of his grog
On the floor for the dog
And his soup on the top of his thighs.

You should be able to come up with a limerick or two. You will need three rhyming words for the long lines, and two rhyming words for the short lines. Take one of your favorite (or un-favorite) persons and write a limerick about them. You might find out that a friend of yours succumbed to a common boyhood temptation, and write:

There once was a boy named Bobby
Who had a peculiar hobby.
He'd get sick, it's no joke,
On cigar butts he'd smoke,
That he'd find in the City Hall lobby.

Or you might have a teacher that drives you up the wall:

There once was a teacher, Miss Tanner,
Who has an unspeakable manner.
She murmurs and mumbles,
Then complains and grumbles
When the poor kids just can't understanner.

Go ahead, try it. You'll like it!

There once was a _____
Who _____
She/He _____

There once was a _____
Who _____
She/He _____

There once was a _____
Who _____
She/He _____

There once was a _____
Who _____
She/He _____

PUNS

Puns have been called "the lowest form of humor". I don't know who said that. But I suspect it was someone who wasn't very successful at thinking up puns. It can be tough and challenging at times to come up with a pun, at other times they seem to come up like spontaneous combustion.

(Forgive me.) One thing I do know, though: Puns are most often more amusing to the punster than to the listener. Puns are usually greeted with groans rather than laughter, but other punsters and closet punsters* will remember good ones for later repetition. Puns are simply the substitution of

*People who pretend not be be punsters, but really are.

55

words having the same or nearly the same sounds for other words with different meanings. For example:

A history professor, recounting Hitler's invasion of Russia for the purpose of acquiring "Lebensraum" for the German people, said, "You might say he took steppes to give his people some living space."

Or, for better or worse:

Two gentlemen in London were discussing the servant problem. One said to the other, "I must say, your maid has imperious airs. Every time I ask her to do something, she simply stares me down." The other replied, "Oh, don't mind her, she's just our down-stares maid."

Can you recall puns that you have heard? Can you remember a pun or two that you might have inflicted on some poor soul? Try to come up with a pun or two right now. It won't be easy, unless you are surrounded by conditions that will spark them. It's a better idea to keep your eyes open for punny situations . . . and go for the groans.

_____
_____
_____
_____
_____
_____
_____
_____
_____
_____
_____
_____
_____

57

Each of the following cartoons is filled with fodder for a punster. I challenge you to come up with at least two puns per picture!

_____
_____
_____
_____
_____
_____
_____
_____
_____

Do you accept my challenge?

Once you've come up with your own puns, turn to Page 60 and check some suggestions.

Some suggestions for puns on Pages 58 and 59:

Cartoon - Page 58:

King *rains* (tears) and King *reigns.*

Horse is *rained* in.

Cartoon - Page 59:

Whaling women and *Wailing* women (note name of boat)

Peg (girl at left) has a *peg* leg.

KNOCK-KNOCKS
THE PUNS' COUNTRY COUSINS

As far as I know, the knock-knock jokes started during the Great Depression. America was so unhappy, it desperately seized on all kinds of humor. Knock-knocks have gone through a number of revivals since, and are now firmly in place as a classic type of American humor. As time goes by, new names appear in the knock-knocks, and time-worn ones disappear. They're really quite simple to compose, and go something like this:

Knock-knock.
Who's there?
Shirley.
Shirley who?
Shirley you don't think I'd give my right name!

or:

Knock-knock.
Who's there?
John.
John who?
John the Navy and see the world.

or:

Knock-knock.
Who's there?
Juan.
Juan who?
Juan of these days, POW! Right in the kisser!

or:

Knock-knock.
Who's there?
Hoo-hoo.
Hoo-hoo Who?
What are you, an owl?

There's another group of knock-knocks that are tied to songs.

For example:

Knock-knock.
Who's there?
Yasser.
Yasser who?
Yasser, that's my baby!

or:

Knock-knock.
Who's there?
Kissinger.
Kissinger who?
I wonder who's Kissinger now?

or:

Knock, knock.
Who's there?
Burton.
Burton who?
Burton up your overcoat when the wind blows
free.

or:

Knock-knock.
Who's there?
Jose.
Jose, can you see by the dawn's early light?

or:

Knock-knock.
Who's there?
Sam and Janet.
Sam and Janet who?
Sam and Janet evening, you may see a
stranger . . .

or:

Knock-knock.
Who's there?
Emma.
Emma who?
Emma gonna have trouble with you, too?

or:

Knock-knock.
Who's there?
Dwain.
Dwain who?
Dwain in Spain stays mainwy in the pwain.

You've surely got the idea by now, so you can try composing some yourself. First, run through every name you can think of, and try to fit it into a knock-knock. Then, try the reverse; think of a popular song title or key phrase of a song or poem, and see if any name pops out of it.

Knock-knocks are a good group activity. Each person in turn starts with:

Knock-knock.
The group in unison: *Who's there?*
Caesar.
The group in unison: *Caesar who?*
Then, the group fires possible answers at the composer until the group solves it or gives up.

Give up?
Caesar the times that try men's souls.

And now, dear readers, we come to the *non sequitur* knock-knock. (You could look it up.) I would advise you to use it sparingly, and only if you have friends with off-the-wall senses of humor. The *non*

sequitur knock-knocks only work when everyone has been stretching their minds to the limit composing and solving knock-knocks! I still remember the occasion when I came up with the example below. A group of us were marooned in a fly-in fishing camp in northern Ontario, and we had turned to knock-knocks for an evening's entertainment. The group was divided into three almost-equal parts after the punch line; those who stared blankly into space, those who thought it was hilarious, and those who wanted to kill me. Here goes:

Knock-knock.
Who's there?
I dreamt I dwelt in marble halls.
I dreamt I dwelt in marble halls who?
I dreamt I dwelt in marble halls Kowalski.

Which group did you join?

Gee, Heather, you've GOT GReat KNOCK-KNOCKS!

was it something I said?

66

It's your turn, again.

Knock-knock.
Who's there?
Shelly.
Shelly who?

_____

Knock-knock.
Who's there?
Daniel.
Daniel who?

_____

Knock-knock.
Who's there?
Rumpelstiltskin.
Rumpelstiltskin who?

_____

Knock-knock.
Who's there?
Shakespeare.
Shakespeare who?

_____

Knock-knock.
Who's there?
The Beatles.
The Beatles who?

_____

Knock-knock.
Who's there?

_____

_____ *who?*
To be, or not to be, that is the question.

Knock-knock.
Who's there?

_____

_____ *who?*
Happy birthday to you, happy birthday to you.

Knock-knock.
Who's there?

_____

_____ *who?*
Row, row, row your boat, gently down the stream.

Knock-knock.
Who's there?

_____

_____ *who?*
Ask not what you can do for your country . . .

Knock-knock.
Who's there?

_____

_____ *who?*
The eyes of Texas are upon you.

WHIMSY

I guess whimsy is my favorite kind of humor. That's mostly because either animals talk, or one's fantasy may soar to such heights as outer space, where even inhabitants of other worlds speak. The strange part, of course, is that they speak languages common to the third planet from the sun, Terra (or is it called Earth now?)

The other nice thing about whimsy is that it is usually non-destructive, doesn't attack people or delight in their discomfiture, and is only rarely insulting of some animal's intelligence or personal habits.

An example of whimsy:

> One day a boy leads his dog into the local malt shop. When he orders a malt, the clerk asks him if he has any money. He says, "I've got something better than money; I've got a talking dog. For a vanilla malt, I'll have him talk for you." The clerk agrees, and serves the malt. When he's done, the boy pats the stool next to him and says, "C'mon, Rover, up here." The dog jumps up on the stool and looks at his master's face expectantly.
> "Now, Rover, what do you call the top of a house?"
> "Roof!" the dog barked loudly.

"Good! Now, when you weave cloth, the threads going one way are called the 'warp', what are the threads going the other way called?"

"Woof!" barked the dog.

"Good boy!" Of course, the warp and the woof!" He glanced apprehensively at the soda clerk, who did not seem amused.

A little nervously now, he asked "Who was the greatest home run hitter of all time?"

The dog paused for a moment, then barked out "Ruth!"

Disgusted, the clerk grabbed the boy and the dog, and threw them out the door.

Disconsolate, the dog looked up at his master and said, "I'm sorry, I meant to say 'Aaron'!"

That's whimsical!

Just for that, I'm sending you to the farm league — with them chickens, cows, and goats!

70

Often, the fact of an animal speaking is funny in itself, so that a joke wouldn't work if humans said the same things. Sometimes animal jokes work because animals exhibit unexpected human traits. Example:

A preacher finds the town drunk lying in the gutter with a big pig.
The preacher says, "That's right, you're only fit to live with pigs!"
Whereupon, the pig gets up and walks away.

Another example:

A newly successful young man, knowing that his widowed mother is lonely back in the old home town, buys the most expensive pet he can find to keep her company — a parrot with a vocabulary of over 2,000 words. *The note he receives, far from being a thank-you note, merely complains that after she had plucked and roasted the crazy-colored chicken, it was so scrawny and tough, it wasn't worth the effort. Aghast, he calls his mother long distance. "Mother, how could you kill and eat that bird?! I paid $5,000 for it! It was so smart, it had a vocabulary of over 2,000 words!" The mother, non-plussed, simply asked, "If it was so smart, why didn't it say something?"*

Of course, this is reverse whimsy. The only way the crazy-colored chicken could have saved itself was by pleading with the old lady.

A golden oldie:

A stranger beholds a wondrous sight in the town square. A bloodhound is playing checkers with a man in overalls. The stranger walks up, just as the dog makes a triple jump over his opponent. "That's got to be the smartest dog I've ever seen," he blurts out. "Nah," comes the reply, "Been playin' against him for years, and he's only beat me five or six times."

Now, how about you? Do you have a whimsical bent? Can you invent a joke giving some animal the power of speech or some other human talent? You can if you try. I'll give you a couple of whimsical creatures to start with, and you come up with the joke.

KMOO-TV

...AND NOW, THE NEWS....

CARICATURES & CARTOONS

I've included both caricatures and cartoons in this section because they are often confused, and in truth, often overlap.

A caricature is a sketch of a person which exaggerates distinctive features, or peculiarities, to the point of instant recognition. Hitler's mustache and forelock are classic examples, as are Jimmy Carter's grin, Elton John's sunglasses, Dolly Parton's figure, John Wayne's lurching gait. A caricature can be produced on paper, or canvas, or done on stage or on camera. We'll concentrate on the pen and paper type of caricature, although you may choose pencil, crayon, or chalk.

If you have a friend with a persistent cowlick, for instance, a recognizable portrait can be drawn with only limited artistic skill, provided you exaggerate the cowlick in the hair. A girl with bangs and glasses is a quick and easy subject for caricature. Perhaps your subject is the center on the basketball team, tall and thin with curly hair. A virtual stick figure with elongated limbs and a mop of curly hair may be instantly recognizable.

Cartoons, on the other hand, may have characters with no recognizable identity. In fact, they need not even be animate. Two rocks can converse in cartoons. A refinement of cartoons is the cartoon strip in which a time sequence is represented with successive actions or utterances.

The overlap of caricature and cartoon occurs when you wish to put a recognizable character into the cartoon. A caricature is usually used rather than a painstakingly drawn portrait, and serves the purpose just as well.

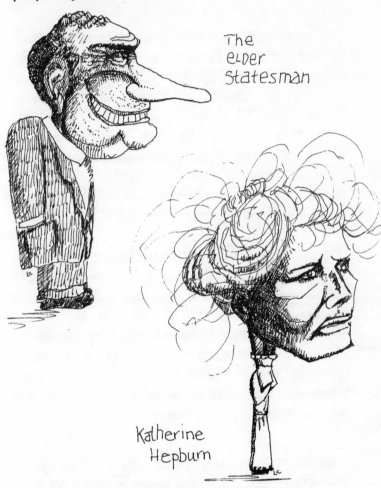

The elder statesman

Katherine Hepburn

We probably get more individual humor bits each day from the cartoons in our daily paper than from any other single source. The modern newspaper usually has one page almost full of single-and multiple-panel cartoons (we call the multiple-panel cartoons comic strips), and one, two or several more cartoons scattered through the pages. The editorial page often has a political cartoon, which usually pokes fun at a world or national figure. Of course, the Sunday paper almost always has a whole section of cartoons and comic strips in color.

What is a cartoon? The single-panel cartoon is almost always a scene from a play, the character or characters frozen in time. The stage background may be elaborate in detail, stylized, or bare. The character(s) may be drawn in great detail, simple line drawing, or as a stick drawing. With the scene set, the character(s) in place, we usually get one line of dialogue, or one line from each character. Sometimes the words appear in "balloons" over the speaker's head, sometimes in print below the cartoon.

The nicest thing about cartoon humor is that anyone can draw a cartoon. A real artist can set the stage in elaborate detail, even show expressions on faces. A so-so sketcher can manage a line drawing and some background settings. A non-artist like me can get along by using stick figures. Before you put down stick figures, remember that they can convey a lot of expression with very simple treatment. If you wanted to do a cartoon about the basketball coach, and he had the biggest feet in school, you could get your point across by drawing a stick figure with huge feet. If a girl had the frizziest hair in school, you could represent her using a stick figure with wild, coiled lines coming out of its head. And the face can show emotions with very little embellishment.

The examples above could show (left to right) happiness, sadness, exhaustion or concern, stern disapproval, bewilderment, angelic behavior.

80

Some other examples:

"What do you mean, you dropped *my* ice cream cone?"

"Did anyone here find a five-dollar bill?"

Voila! You've got a cartoon!

Practice coming up with good punch lines and getting your cartoon characters to match the action or stance required. Remember, that's all a cartoon is: a line of dialogue delivered in a set scene situation.

Now, try your hand on some incident you know of or have heard of:

Now, try your hand at caricature. Mentally run through your friends and family, analyzing each person for some recognizable characteristic that, when drawn, will instantly identify that person. Many people in your acquaintance will not lend themselves to caricature, but here and there you will find one.

1. _____   2. _____

3. _____

1.

2.

3.

Next, compose a cartoon, using first inanimate objects: two rocks, a rock and a flower, two flowers, two clouds. Next, try your hand at a cartoon with two or more people in it. Can you include your caricature subject in a cartoon? It might be more fun if you can.

1.

2.

EMBELLISHMENTS IN HUMOR

Much of the skill of the true humorist is in the wise use of embellishment. Just as the chef adorns your plate with a sprig of parsley or a slice of candied apple, the skilled humorist uses just the right amount of embellishment. Let me give you an example familiar to all:

You've heard the old two-liner that goes *"Why do firemen wear red suspenders?"*

"To hold their pants up."

The one word that makes this a joke is the word *"red"*. Drop that word, and the humor is lost:

"Why do firemen wear suspenders?"
"To hold their pants up."

Nothing. Now, even in the first example, that little word *"red"* is liable to get lost. So you embellish it a bit with a sprig of verbal parsley.

85

"Why do firemen wear bright red suspenders?"

Now, you've got the listeners' attention. Why **bright** red indeed? Tension builds, and the innocuous answer occasions a chuckle. You can over-embellish, of course:

"Why do left-handed firemen wear bright red suspenders with brass buckles on them?"

It's a case of over-kill.

When re-telling a joke you've heard, a little tasteful embellishment is often a good idea. In order to build listener interest, give the Englishman a monocle, the country bumpkin overalls, the city slicker yellow shoes, the eastern dude a derby, the cowboy a six-gun as long as a sheep's leg, an old horse a swayed back, a cat a squinty eye. You'll be drawing the picture a little clearer. Building the tension of expectation a little higher, assuring a greater reaction at the punch line.

Think over the jokes you can remember. Couldn't some of them use a little embellishment before you file them back in your memory, ready for later use?

Joke: _____

_____

_____

Embellishments: _____

_____

_____

_____

DON'T LIKE THE MOVIES?
WRITE YOUR OWN!

You've probably noticed that there have been a whole series of movies where humanity is threatened by nature gone wild (The Killer Bees), nature being itself (Jaws), or nature being unnatural (The Blob). The screen writers have used a formula, with or without romantic sub-plot, that goes something like this:

1) A seemingly innocuous event takes place without anyone paying particular attention, which will set the stage for what is to come. (A meteorite lands in a tomato patch; a girl swimmer disappears; a dust ball is sucked into a vacuum cleaner.)

2) The menace grows, comes to the attention of the public (or authorities), and threatens to overwhelm the population.

88

3) The situation looks hopeless. A brave scientific team of specialists is brought in. This tea always includes the most handsome man in the movie and a gorgeous young lady, who is either the daughter of an eminent scientist (always played by Burgess Meredith), or has a Ph.D. in her own right.

The U.S. Army also appears, offering to put a stop to the menace by brute force. (Strangely, the army usually consists of a general, a sergeant, six soldiers, a jeep, and two hundred feet of World War II training film.)

send in a messenger Through enemy Lines - send in Peggy Fleming!

4) After the army fails to stop it, or them, ("The rockets don't seem to have any effect, sir!" "But, Sergeant, they're the most powerful weapons we have!") the scientists come up with an amazingly simple solution which dissolves (disintegrates),

repels, kills) the menace. They use salt water (fresh water, ultrasonic waves, microwave transmissions, old Elvis Presley records). Humanity is saved!

You, too, can save humanity. The formula is available, its commercial value assured. All one needs to do is plug in the right elements, and another successful screen writer is born.

Here's a home-made version.

Opening Scene:

Mrs. Forester, looking like she just came from a beauty salon, comes downstairs to the kitchen to start breakfast. As she enters the kitchen, she sees the refrigerator door is ajar, the refrigerator is filled with ice cubes, and about four bushels of cubes have spilled onto the floor. Mr. Forester follows her into the kitchen and unplugs the refrigerator. Obviously, the icemaker has gone wild, and she promises to call the repairman.

Fade to the title:

CUBES — THE FROZEN TIDE THAT THREATENED TO ENGULF THE WORLD

90

The next night, the refrigerator, supposedly repaired, waits until the family has gone to bed, then opens its door and starts producing tons of ice cubes. The ice cubes spill out, go across the floor, up the stairs, into father's bed, and begin to freeze him in his sleep. Mrs. Forester opens her eyes to see a wall of ice cubes advancing towards her. She

*grabs a robe, drags the semi-conscious Mr. Forester out of the **other** bedroom door (Don't all bedrooms have two doors?), and wakens Jimmy and Dorothy. They escape out a window to the porch roof, jump to the ground, and run to the house next door. The neighbors are skeptical until ice cubes come spewing out of all the windows and doors, and the house disintegrates. They all jump into the neighbors' station wagon. It doesn't start, and the wall of ice is piling up against the back of* the station wagon. The women and children scream, and the wagon finally starts. They escape.

Now there are a series of scenes showing the ice advancing, rivers and lakes drying up as the ice thirstily converts them to ice. The White House is informed, the U.S. Army is mobilized (all eight of them) and the scientific team arrives at the next big city in the path of the ice.

After several futile attempts at stopping the ice, the beautiful young thing says; "I've got it! What does it take to make ice?"

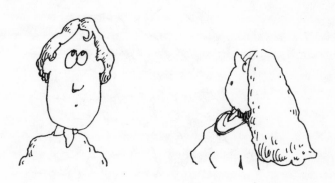

Everybody replies, "Water. But it's got all of that it needs. It's even tapped underground streams."

"Yes, but don't you see? It needs electricity! If we could shut down every power plant, every wind mill, every solar array, every dam and automobile in the country for a period of twenty-four hours, we could stop it!"

92

So we have a series of scenes of people throwing huge switches with sound effects of whining machinery winding down to silence, pictures of dams with the water flow stopped, people turning off their cars and walking away. Then we have a picture from space, showing the lights going out all over the North American continent.

Scene 2:

The next scene is at the command post. Present are the U.S. Army (all eight of them), the team of scientists (the handsome young man and the beautiful Ph.D. now very much in love) and the Foresters; Mom, Dad, Jimmy and Dorothy. Mr. Forester, it turns out, is chief engineer of a huge utility, a former classmate of the handsome scientist, and the only man in the entire U.S. who knows every connection in the North American power grid. They wait in the darkness, cut off from retreat, as a wall of cubes, fifty feet high, appears at the next intersection and advances towards them. The ice is just feet from their window and they can feel its chill. They wait for the end.
Finally, Jimmy says; "I don't think it's advanced any in the last hour." The scientist cries; "You're right, Jimmy! Look! At the base of the pile! Water! It's melting!"

Now we have stock film footage of every flood since the great Johnstown flood, showing the water flowing from the sea. The satellite shot shows the lights going back on all over North America. (Actually we just run the other film backwards.) Machinery whines into action, dams start spewing water, people start their cars. Life returns to normal, and the Foresters get a call from the White House telling them that a grateful America will rebuild their house.

The last shot shows the Foresters having a dinner party in their rebuilt house for the scientific team, the U.S. Army (all eight of them) and the next-door neighbors (actually almost the entire cast), and Jimmy remarks that his water is warm.

Mrs. Forester says; "Sorry about that, Jimmy, but our new refrigerator doesn't have an ice maker."

All smile.

Fade.

Now, if I can put *"CUBES"* together, you can certainly write a horror film of your own. Some topics might be:

"Books" — the books in a high school library band together to stop the damaging of books by students, first cornering the worst kid in school, crushing him to death, then returning to their shelves. This goes on for some time, baffling the police, until a beautiful young librarian (who is in love with the handsome vice-principal who is about to lose his job because of these incidents) notices that the books are in different locations on different days. She telephones the vice-principal (boy, how dumb can you get?) and while he is on his way, they try to get her. When he arrives, she is up to her shoulders in books, screaming, but he gets her out by breaking a window. The books are burned.

*"**Clean Up.**" Where a young kid finally gives in to a mother's repeated demands that the bedroom be cleaned up. Unbeknownst to the child, the stuff has been lying around so long, it has taken on a life of its own and resists his attempt. It's most fearsome weapon: the fifteen sox under the bed.*

QUICK MOM — GET THE VACUUM CLEANER!

*"**Filter**" — swimming pools start devouring swimmers and digesting them in their filtration systems. Even I can't come up with a solution to that. Maybe you can.*

*"**Lips**" — a monstrous carp takes over the swimming hole and threatens to wipe out the youth population of the entire town. The solution: the town's best fisherman goes after it with a giant construction crane for a fishing pole, a yacht anchor for a hook and an eight-foot diameter dough ball for bait. The carp almost topples the huge crane in its battling, but the fisherman finally prevails.*

96

Now, you're on your own.

Hm-m-m.

"Noodles" — In this Chinese Restaurant, a beautiful young Chinese girl . . .

PICTURESQUE SPEECH-SIMILES

Similes can be humorous or not, depending on their content, but they **can** be fun to compose, and can make your conversations or writings more interesting and more descriptive. Similes simply compare one thing with another, in order to make a comparison or illustration. For instance, if you wanted to describe a tyrannical teacher in a way that means her style is a near disaster, you might say, "She runs the class like Captain Bligh ran the Bounty." In that short phrase, you can say a lot about that teacher, the temper of the students, and the general value of the class as an educational experience. It also relieves tension by discussing the problem in a humorous vein. She'll probably never be put over the side of the ship in a little boat, but maybe she should be.

Burnt Toast?

He flew through the air like a piece of burnt toast!

99

If you lived in a community that knew about keeping horses, you might describe an athlete the worse for wear by saying, "He looks like a horse that's been ridden hard and put away wet." In a community that doesn't know horses, your humor would be lost.

Similes must fit the audience. It doesn't do any good to attempt to illustrate a point if the simile is incomprehensible to the reader or listener. This is not to say that similes can't resort to fantasy. "Her smile was like an angel's kiss," or "His glance was like a jab from a devil's pitchfork."

Similes also have a way of aging to a point they are no longer funny. I always liked the ending " . . . looked like World War II . . . (pause) . . . with the original cast." It had all kinds of applications which I thought hilarious. But new generations have come along and World War II is neither familiar, comprehensible nor potentially humorous to them. So I use that old chestnut only among people over fifty. Hard as it may be to believe, there **were** humorous aspects to World War II, (although it wasn't as hilarious as Hogan's Heroes would lead you to believe), and humor did survive the period.

I know two brothers from Missouri. They share the distinction in my mind as being the two most picturesque speakers I've ever known. I wish I could remember a few things I've heard them say over the years, but their words melted like snow flakes in my mind. (Get the simile?) But one line will stay with me forever: "He just stomped up to her like a burnt-toed rooster . . ." Now **that's** a simile! I've carried a mental picture of just how that character walked up to whomever he was confronting. My mental picture will be different from yours, since I suspect neither of us has ever seen a burnt-toed rooster; nor are we likely to see one. But I'm sure you'll agree that as an image-conjurer, it's great!

We can probably come up with our own "burnt toes". How about, "He swam like a broken-tailed eel," or "She moved like a Mack truck with a broken axle," or "Her voice sounded like a chain saw with a loose muffler."?

Try some similes from scratch. You probably already use them several times a day. Come on, listen, will you? Oh, I give up. Trying to convince you is like talking to a . . . !

"My house is like . . .

"My bedroom is like . . .

101

"My kid brother/sister is like . . .

"Our school is like . . .

"His hair is like . . .

"He kicks a football like . . .

"She dances like . . .

Then, branch out a little:

"Talking to that teacher is like . . .

"Trying to get him to do something is like . . .

"Cleaning my room is like . . .

"Playing chess with him is like . . .

"Buying a magazine on chess is like . . .

"Staying away from junk food is like . . .

STEREOTYPES IN HUMOR
Sometimes Funny, Sometimes Not So Funny

I recently read an article in **Scientific American** magazine about an ancient Hellenic city unearthed in southern Russia. The diggers found a waterspout with a familiar face, a copy of the grinning mask of the cook-slave of traditional Greek drama. Even in the fourth century B.C., certain stereotypes in humor were sufficiently established that they were copied in another art form.

Students of Greek literature and drama can tell us today the traits embodied in this stereotype from long ago. Stereotypes still exist, of course. The broad humor of the TV show "Hee!Haw!" could not sustain itself if the actors spoke with New York

103

accents and wore New York fashions. The show capitalizes on and reinforces certain stereotypes identified with the Southern rural areas. The next time you watch the show, spend a little time picking out the uses of stereotypes in enhancing humor on the show. Save your list, and watch another segment at a later date. Note which stereotypes are repeated, and note some others either overlooked in the earlier segment, or introduced for the first time.

The same stereotypical approach to humor may be found in "action" television series, such as "The Dukes of Hazzard", to while away the time between car chases and to help lighten the inevitable conflicts between the heroes and law enforcement officers. Old-time series such as "Green Acres" and "Beverly Hillbillies" fed on the same approach, with each actor bound by the stereotype of the role played, segment after segment.

Much of our present-day humor depends on stereotypes. Mother-in-law jokes, for instance, would fall flat if it were not for the established mental image of meddling, ill-tempered mothers-in-law. Younger brothers are the bane of a young woman's existence during courtship, at least in our humorous tradition. TV comedy fathers are usually fumbling, bumbling masses of ineptitude, saved in segment after segment by practical, intelligent wives or precocious children. Did you ever wonder how those incompetent fathers could earn enough to pay for the huge houses they live in?

Stereotypes are often established by "typecasting", or by popular heroes in literature, drama, radio, movies or TV. The radio (later TV) series "Amos and Andy" established several misleading stereotypes of black persons among people who had little contact with the black population. The jokes of Jewish comedians that for years were intended to poke gentle fun at members of the Jewish community, and were appreciated with glee by Jews, helped engender certain stereotypical images in the minds of persons who had little or no contact with people of Jewish heritage. The use of stereotypes, while promoting humor in many instances, should not be used to demean or embarrass any segment of our population.

The well-known ethnic jokes capitalize on stereotypes. I used to be rather embarrassed by ethnic jokes until I heard the *same* joke repeated about a wide variety of peoples as I travelled around the country. You know, *every* nationality,

DID YOU Hear the one about the Chinese Cartoonist who illustrated this book?...

race, creed or area has its statistical share of persons who embody every vice and every virtue. The saving grace to it all is that, time after time, I've heard members of one group or another telling the same jokes about members of *their* group with great delight. And do you know what? The students of Texas A&M, the "Aggies", have been the butt of virtually every "ethnic" joke I've ever heard.

When TV watching becomes a bit boring, you might try keeping an eye out for the use of stereotypes. Are blondes really that dumb? Are big guys mental pygmies? In war stories like "Hogan's Heroes", does "our side" have all the brains?

BLONDES ARE NOT DUMB!
We're just as smart
as any other high school
drop out

106

Describe, in 30 words or less, the stereotype of each of the following:

Type Show: **Character:**
Soap Opera   *Betrayed partner*
Description:

_____

_____

_____

_____

_____

_____

_____

_____

_____

Type Show: **Character:**
Quiz Show   *Host*
Description:

_____

_____

_____

_____

_____

_____

_____

_____

_____

Type Show: **Character:**

Medical Show   *Young, up-and-coming*
Doctor

Description:

_____

_____

_____

_____

_____

_____

_____

_____

_____

_____

Type Show: **Character:**

News   *Hard-hitting Reporter*

Description:

_____

_____

_____

_____

_____

_____

_____

_____

_____

_____

Type Show: **Character:**
Situation Comedy   *Snooping Neighbor*
Description:

_____
_____
_____
_____
_____
_____
_____
_____
_____
_____

Type Show: **Character:**
Police Story   *Tag-along News Reporter*
Description:

_____
_____
_____
_____
_____
_____
_____
_____
_____
_____

Give examples from actual TV shows that fit your stereotype of these stereotypes.

What would happen if these characters acted entirely different than the stereotype? How about a Quiz Show host acting like Barbara Walters?

_____
_____
_____
_____
_____
_____
_____
_____
_____
_____
_____
_____
_____
_____
_____
_____
_____
_____
_____
_____
_____
_____

SLAPSTICK HUMOR
And Other Forms of Violence

You've heard of slapstick comedy, I'm sure, and you probably associate it with the Three Stooges and similar old movie comedy. It actually started on the stage long before movies came along. In fact, it was the need to communicate with the theater audience that led to the invention of the device that gave that type of comedy its name: the slapstick. The slapstick looks like a cricket bat. It is made of two thin boards, bound or glued together only at the handle. When it was applied to a person's body (usually on the backside), the two thin boards slapped together as loudly as a firecracker. (Thus, the name.) Of course, the audiences loved it. The sound effects added a note of hilarity to the pummeling that went on in stage comedy. (There's really not all that much humor in someone being thudded by a cricket bat. But an audience responds to the crack! Or a slapstick.

There has always been an undertone of violence in much of stage and screen comedy. Pratfalls have been standard fare, even though there's nothing funny about a cracked tailbone.

Movie cameras gave us a closer look at the comedians than was available to most of the theater audience, so physical violence could be simpler, and on a smaller scale. The stage demanded broad gestures, sweeping blows; the movie camera followed with fingers in the eyes, stepping on toes, slaps to the top of a bald head.

We might like to think that we see so much through the lens of the television and movie cameras that we have become too sophisticated to enjoy slapstick humor. Although comedy producers of today have come to that conclusion as well, the Three Stooges are enjoying a renaissance right now, eye pokes, head slaps, and all.

Many of the old comedies had authority figures, policemen, professors, grand dames, who were subjected to all manner of physical violence and degradation, probably reflecting America's growing distaste for the trappings of authority and high society. A lot of actors portraying these roles were subjected to dunkings, white-washings, pie throwings and blows to various parts of their anatomies.

What do you think? Is a bit of physical violence necessary to your appreciation of humor? You can analyze your feelings by watching the old movie comedies on television. The Three Stooges weren't alone in their hands-on comedy, although they probably resorted to it more than any other comedians I can think of. Bud Abbott used to cuff Lou Costello now and then. (In fact, I think that's where the line, "Thanks, I needed that!" came from.) And there was always the feeling that Laurel feared physical violence from the bigger, grimmer Hardy in their comedies.

THE ULTIMATE CRAZINESS OR THE PHONETIC STORY

I've saved the best for last. You are about to tackle a dual challenge. The first part will require that you interpret the story below, the second will require that you write a story yourself. Sounds easy? Not when you consider that the stories must be written without using a single word in its proper place. When read aloud, the substitute words should approximate the sounds of the proper words. You might have to change the accent on some words. For instance, the third word in the example should not be pronounced a'tom, but a-tom'; it'll help a lot. Another example "wassail" is correctly pronounced like wah'-sell, so "wassail emanated" becomes "was eliminated". Words run into each other, and "ecu doughnut" becomes "he could not". Okay, take it from there.

Won't supine atom, dare veer tree ladle pegs. Juan belt hiss hose ups draw, hun ess souse offs decks, hen deferred bull teas awes audio brigs. Deforest dew vanished tare rouses any ewery, hen dents surround hands hung, "Ooze affray dada baghdad roof?" Buddy ways dirt peg sat, "Aisle macaw hussy brigand murder." Andy dead.

Wander Bagdad roof came roan, day pegs wren tudor roams. Juan below, Andy verse douse varnished. Wander roof bluer ganders egg hound cordage days ender graded.

Bud Wendy oar able roof game tudor brigand murder rouse, see worse dumped. Nomad drowse sea dried, ecu doughnut bloody austin. Heat ride weed Alice mite, Buddy coon dirt dad Brigand murder rouse! Vine Leahy claim Donner hoof hands led honor Jim any. Body dirt peg dder bag far inner voyeur plays. Soda roof wassail emanated. Nodder peg stanchion sink, "Ooze affray dada Baghdad roof, Baghdad roof, Baghdad roof? Ooze affray dada Baghdad roof, draw-loll-loll-loll-lei?"

You can choose any story you please for your own phonetic story. Here are three you might consider:

Czech ender burn stork
Edsel hand griddle
Slip imbue day hander ham thumbprints

Good luck!

Ah, cut the GIBBERISH and talk pig latin!

ANUDDER JOQUE

A fellow walked into a restaurant with a twelve-foot alligator on a leash. After a great deal of tugging and pushing, he got the alligator under a corner table.

When the waitress timidly approached his table, the man demanded, "Do you serve senior citizens here?" "Of course," was the surprised reply. "Good, give my alligator a senior citizen, and I'll have a cheeseburger."

Motivate Minds
and
Maximize Brain Power!

Incorporating results-oriented techniques from the Kathy Kolbe Concept, Think-ercises®
build intellectual fitness by:

- **exercising thinking skills**
- **strengthening self-esteem**
- **building communication skills**
- **generating mental excitement**

Think-ercises are available in a wide range of kid-tested books, games and
activities...preschool through high school. Each Think-ercise develops the whole spec-
trum of learning potential and reinforces basic skills including:

- **math and visual thinking**
- **language arts**
- **science**
- **social studies**
- **arts and humanities**

For a **FREE CATALOG** of idea-
igniting Think-ercises, complete
the coupon below and return to:

Think-ercise, Dept. B
P.O. Box 15050
Phoenix, AZ 85060

**Yes! I want to help kids achieve intellectual fitness with
Think-ercises!**

Please send _____ FREE
☐ Parent catalogs ☐ Educator catalogs to:

Name _____

Address _____

City/State _____ Zip_____

Phone ( ) _____

Age of Children _____

Date _____

Mail to:
Think-ercise, Dept. B, P.O. Box 15050, Phoenix, AZ 85060